100 Jazz & Blues Greats

Exclusive Distributors:
Music Sales Limited,
8/9 Frith Street, London W1V 5TZ, England.
Music Sales Pty, Limited,
120 Rothschild Avenue, Rosebery, NSW 2018, Australia.

This book © Copyright 1987 by Wise Publications.
ISBN 0.7119.1200.9
Order No. AM 66614

Designed by Pearce Marchbank Studio.

Music Sales complete catalogue lists thousands of titles and is free from
your local music book shop, or direct from Music Sales Limited.
Please send a cheque or Postal Order for £1.50 for postage to Music Sales Limited,
8/9 Frith Street, London W1V 5TZ.

Printed in Great Britain by Redwood Books, Trowbridge, Wiltshire

Wise Publications

Caravan

By Duke Ellington, Irving Mills & Juan Tizol

Sleep _____ up-on my shoul-der as we creep _____ A-cross the sands so I may keep _____ This mem-'ry of our CAR-A-VAN _____

This _____ is so ex - cit - - ing _____

You _____ are so in - vit - - ing _____

Rest - - ing in my arms _____ As I

thrill to the mag - ic charms _____ of

Oh! Look At Me Now

Words by John DeVries
Music by Joe Bushkin

brand new start, __ I'm so proud I'm bust-in' my vest. __
Gon-na be Mis - iz, not Miss. __

So,

I am the guy __ who turned out a lov - er, So, I'm the guy, __ who
(girl) __ (girl) __

laughed at those blue __ dia-mond rings, __ one of those things, __

__ Oh! Look At Me Now. __ Now. __

Swingin' Shepherd Blues

Words by Rhoda Roberts & Kenny Jacobson
Music by Moe Koffman

VERSE

1. A-long a moun-tain pass, there is a patch of grass where the swing-in' shep-herd plays his tune,
2. (And down the) moun-tain pass, there lives a pret-ty lass who's wait-in' for the moon to shine a-bove,

His sheep nev-er stray, danc-in' all day till they see the
She dress-es with care, braid-in' her hair for her one and

pale and yel-low moon. And then he leads his flock and home-ward
on-ly swing-in' love. And she knows he'll nev-er roam be-cause she

they all rock to the tune of The Swing-in' Shep-herd Blues.
waits at home for the tune of The Swing-in' Shep-herd Blues.

CHORUS

Come home shep - herd, Play those haunt - ing trills. Come home shep herd, Let it ech - o through the hills, The Swing - in' Shep - herd Blues. 2. And down the Blues.

Tuxedo Junction

Words by Buddy Feyne
Music by Erskine Hawkins, William Johnson & Julian Dash

Mean To Me

Words & Music by Roy Turk & Fred E. Ahlert

Satin Doll

Words by Johnny Mercer
Music by Duke Ellington & Billy Strayhorn

BIG BAND MID 3 @ 100 (Needs
(Practice)

Sophisticated Lady

Words by Irving Mills & Mitchell Parish
Music by Duke Ellington

changed you some - how I see you now Laugh - ing, dar - ing,

ne - ver car - ing that you hurt me like you do, bright eyes shin - ing,

ne - ver pin - ing For a love that is fond and true, Tho' such love was meant for you Poor____ so - phis - ti -

- ca - ted la - dy, I know____ you miss the love you lost long a - go,____ And when no -

- bo - dy is nigh you cry. _____ They cry. _____

Blues In The Night (My Mama Done Tol' Me)

Words by Johnny Mercer
Music by Harold Arlen

blues _____ in the night, Now the rain's a-fall-in', hear the train a-call-in', whoo-ee, _____ (My

ma-ma done tol' me, _____) Hear dat lone-some whis-tle blow - in' 'cross the tres-tle, whoo-ee, _____ (My

ma-ma done tol' me, _____)A whoo-ee-duh-whoo-ee, _____ Ol' click-e-ty clack's a-ech-o-in' back th'

blues _____ in the night,_The eve-nin' breeze - 'll start the trees to cry-in' and the

STAND SWING ♩. 149
OR SHUFFLE R'N'ROLL

Opus One

Words & Music by Sy Oliver

JAZZ BALL 3 1/2 3@ 79

Solitude

Words by Eddie de Lange & Irving Mills
Music by Duke Ellington

sit in my chair, I'm filled with de - spair, There's no one could be so sad ____ With

gloom ev-'ry-where, I sit and I stare, I know that I'll soon go mad In my

SOL - I - TUDE ____ I'm pray - ing Dear Lord a - bove ____

_ Send back my love. In my love. _____

Slow Soul Ball

Mood Indigo

Words & Music by Duke Ellington, Irving Mills & Albany Bigard

CHORUS

Slow

Al-ways get that mood in-di-go,_ Since my ba-by said good - bye,

In tl. eve - nin' when lights are low._ I'm so lone-some I could cry,

'Cause there's no-bo-dy who cares a-bout me,_ I'm just a soul who's blu-er than blue can be,

When I get that mood in-di-go,_ I could lay me down and die. die.

Blue And Sentimental

Words & Music by Count Basie, Jerry Livingston & Mack David

September Song

Words by Maxwell Anderson
Music by Kurt Weill

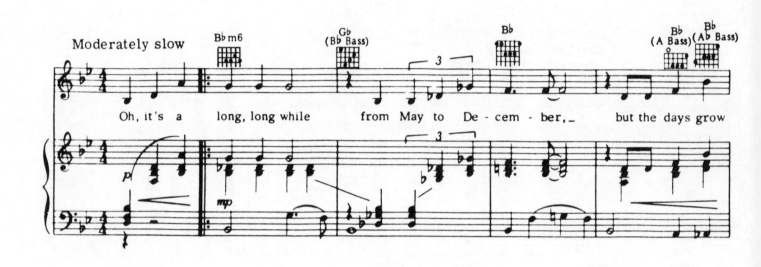

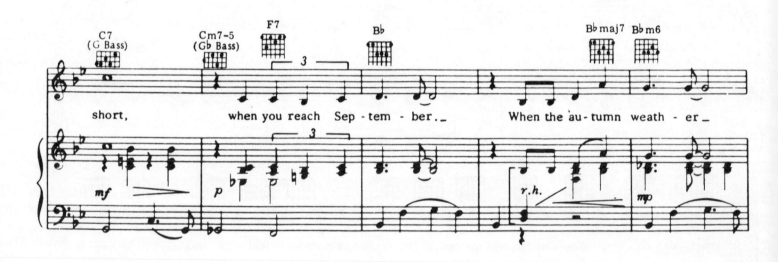

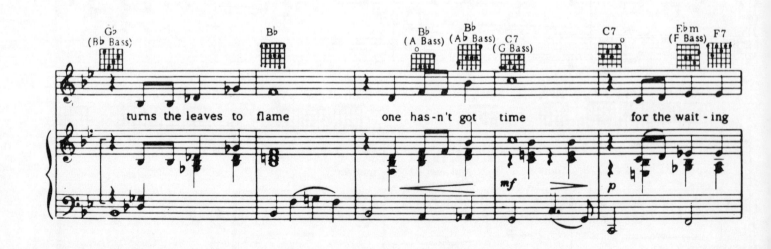

Fly Me To The Moon (In Other Words)

Words & Music by Bart Howard

Round Midnight

Words & Music by Cootie Williams & Thelonious Monk

It be - .gins to tell 'round mid - night, 'round mid - night.

I do pret -ty well till af - ter sun - down.

Sup - per - time, I'm feel - ing sad. But it

real - ly gets bad 'round mid - night.

Mem-'ries al-ways start 'round mid-night, 'round mid-night.

Have-n't got the heart to stand those mem-'ries,

when my heart is still with you,   and old

mid-night knows it too._____   When some

The Very Thought Of You

Words & Music by Ray Noble

Lyrics:

I don't need your pho-to-graph,_____ To keep__ by my bed;
I hold you re-spon-si - ble,_____ I'll take__ it to law,

Your pic - ture is al - ways in__ my head._____
I nev - er have felt like this__ be - fore._____

I don't need your por-trait, dear,_____ To call__ you to mind,_____
I'm su - ing for dam-ag - es,_____ Ex - cus - es won't do,_____

day - dream, I'm hap - py as a king, And fool - ish tho' it may seem, To me that's ev' - ry - thing. The mere i - dea of you, The long - ing here for you, You'll nev - er know how slow the mo - ments go 'till I'm

near to you,_____ I see your face in ev' - ry

flow - er; Your eyes in stars a - bove,____

It's just the thought of you,__ The ver - y thought of you, my love.__

The ver - y love.____

The Wang Wang Blues

Words by Leo Wood
Music by Gus Mueller, Buster Johnson & Henry Busse

Ain't Misbehavin'

Words by Andy Razaf
Music by Thomas Waller & Harry Brooks

CHORUS *Slowly, with expression*

No one to talk with, all by my-self, No one to walk with, but I'm hap-py on the ___ shelf.

Ain't mis-be-hav-in', I'm sav-in' my love for you. ___

I know for cer-tain the one I love, I'm thro' with flirtin', it's just you I'm think-in' of,

Ain't mis-be-hav-in', I'm sav-in' my love for you. ___

52

Like Jack Horner in the cor-ner, don't go no-where, what do I care, Your kiss-es

are worth wait - in' for, be - lieve me, I don't stay out late,

don't care to go, I'm home a-bout eight just me and my ra - di - o, Ain't mis-be-hav-in'

I'm sav-in' my love for you. you.

But Beautiful

Words by Johnny Burke
Music by Jimmy Van Heusen

It Don't Mean A Thing (If It Ain't Got That Swing)

Words by Irving Mills
Music by Duke Ellington

mu - sic,__ There's some-thing else that makes the tune com - plete.

CHORUS

It don't mean a thing, if it ain't got that swing,__ (doo wah, doo wah,

doo wah, doo wah, doo wah,__ doo wah, doo wah, doo wah,) It don't mean a

thing,__ all you got to do is sing, (doo wah, doo wah, doo wah, doo wah, doo wah,__

doo wah, doo wah, doo wah,) It makes no dif-f'rence if ___ it's sweet or hot, ___ Just give that rhy-thm ev-'ry-thing you got, Oh, it don't mean a thing, if it ain't got that swing, ___ (doo wah, doo wah, doo wah, doo wah, doo wah, ___ doo wah, doo wah, doo wah.) It wah.)

Here's That Rainy Day

Words & Music by Johnny Burke & Jimmy Van Heusen

Don't Go To Strangers

Words by Redd Evans
Music by Arther Kent & Dave Mann

Just The Two Of Us

Words & Music by Ralph MacDonald, William Salter & Bill Withers

1. I see the crys-tal rain-drops fall, and the beau-ty of it
2,3. (see additional lyrics)

all is when the sun comes shin-ing through;____

to make those rain-bows in my mind, when I think of you some-

time, and I want to spend__ some time with you._____ Just__ the

Verse 2:
We look for love; no time for tears;
Wasted water's all that is, and it don't make no flowers grow.
Good things might come to those who wait,
But not for those who wait too late;
We've got to go for all we know.
Just the ... *(To Chorus:)*

Verse 3:
I hear the crystal raindrops fall on the window down the hall,
And it becomes the morning dew.
And darling, when the morning comes, and I see the morning sun,
I want to be the one with you.
Just the ... *(To Chorus:)*

Misirlou

English Words by Fred Wise, Milton Leeds & S.K. Russell
Spanish Words by J. Pina   Music by N. Roubanis

Moonglow

Words & Music by Will Hudson, Eddie de Lange & Irving Mills

Limehouse Blues

Words by Douglas Furber
Music by Phil Braham

Oh! Lime-house blues __ I've the real Lime-house blues __

Can't seem to shake __ off those sad Chin-a blues __

Rings on your fin - gers and tears for your crown __ that is the sto -

- ry of old Chin - a - town.

Come Fly With Me

Lyrics by Sammy Cahn
Music by Jimmy Van Heusen

FLY WITH ME!___ Let's take ___ off in ___ the blue! ___

(Once I get you) Up there! ___ Where the air is

rar - i - fied, ___ ___ We'll just glide, ___

___ ___ star - ry - eyed. ___ (Once I get you)

say the words __ and we'll beat the birds __ down to A - ca - pul - co

Bay. It's per - fect for ____ a fly - ing hon - ey -

moon, they say, COME FLY WITH ME! _____ Let's fly! __

____ Let's fly ____ a - way! _____

Angel Eyes

Words by Earl Brent
Music by Matt Dennis

Freely, with expression

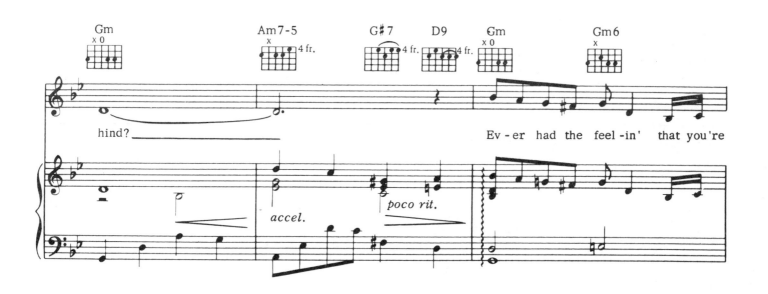

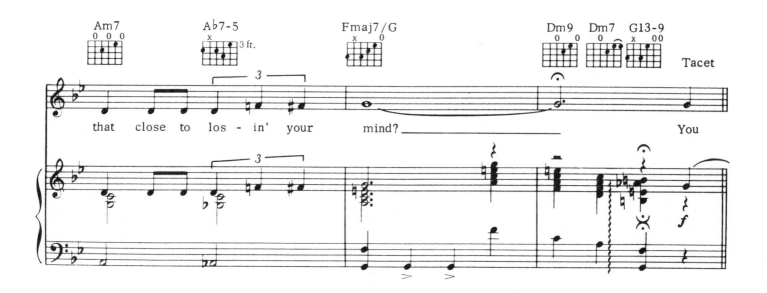

Need I say_ that my love's mis-spent,_ mis - spent with an - gel eyes to - night._

So drink up _____ all you peo - ple,_____

or - der an - y - thing you see. _ Have fun,_____ you hap - py

peo - ple,_____ the drink and the laugh's_ on me._

Back To Earth

Words & Music by Dave Brubeck

Moderately (♩=150)

1st Improvisation

2nd Improvisation

Lullaby Of Birdland

Music by George Shearing
Words by George David Weiss

Learnin' The Blues

Words & Music by Dolores Vicki Silvers

Midnight Sun

Words by Johnny Mercer
Music by Sonny Burke & Lionel Hampton

The Glow-Worm

Composed by Paul Lincke

lit - tle bright-nin', Light_ up, you li'l_ ol' bug of light-nin',
deep and dark - en, You _ and your chick_ should get to spark-in',
took a shine to, Or_ who you're out_ to make a sign to,
glim - mer, (glim-mer,) Shine,_ lit - tle glow-worm, glim - mer! (glim-mer!)

When you got-ta glow, you got - ta glow,_ Glow, lit-tle glow-worm, glow.
I got_ a gal that I love so,_ Glow, lit-tle glow-worm, glow.
I got_ a gal that I love so,_ Glow, lit-tle glow-worm, glow.
Light the path, be - low, a - bove, And lead us on to Love!

Fine for 3rd Chorus

Glow, lit-tle glow - worm,_ Put on a show_ worm,_ Glow, lit - tle

Fine for 4th Chorus

glow - worm, glow. _____ lead us on to Love!

101

The Joint Is Jumpin'

Words by Andy Razaf & J C Johnson
Music by Thomas Waller

This here spot is more than hot, in fact the joint is jump-in'.
Grab a jug and cut the rug, I mean this joint is jump-in'.

Check your weap-ons at the door, be sure to pay your quar-ter.
Get your pig feet, beer and gin, there's plen-ty in the kitch-en.

Burn your leath-er on the floor, grab an-y-bod-y's daugh-ter.
Who is that that just came in? Just look at the way he's switch-in'.

The roof is rock-in', the neigh-bor's knock-in'.
Don't mind the hour, 'cause I'm in pow-er.

105

The Old Piano Roll Blues

Words & Music by Cy Coben

Ragtime Tempo

CHORUS

I wan-na hear it a-gain,_ I wan-na hear it a-gain,_

The Old Pi-a-no Roll Blues._ We're sit-tin' at an up-right, My

sweet-ie and me,_ Push-in' on the ped-als, mak-in' sweet har-mo-ny. When we hear

rink-i-ty tink, And we hear plink-i-ty plink, We cud-dle clos-er, it seems,

And while we kiss, kiss, kiss a - way all our cares, The play-er pia-no's play-in'

razz-a-ma-tazz,— I wan-na hear it a - gain,— I wan-na hear it a - gain,—

The Old Pi - a - no Roll Blues.— I wan-na —

Time's A-Wastin'

Words & Music by Duke Ellington, Mercer Ellington & Don George

While there's a moon up

Can't our song be more than just a tune up?

Late-ly, dar-ling, I have learned a les-son,

More than just my dreams de-sire ca-

-ress-in'

So, hast-en now

'Cause, ba-by, the time is a-wast-in' now.

I Can't Give You Anything But Love

Words by Dorothy Fields
Music by Jimmy McHugh

Tain't Nobody's Biz-Ness If I Do

Words & Music by Porter Grainger & Everett Robbins

*Show version

115

Mercy, Mercy, Mercy

Words by Gail Fisher Levy & Vincent Levy
Music by Josef Zawinul

- cy please don't make___ me beg on bend - ed knees oh please___

___ Mer-cy, Mer-cy, Mer-cy, Please have mer-cy on me.___ Mer-cy, Mer-cy, Mer-cy

f

Interlude

please. { How can I face life with - out you what would I
{ You know I love you I'm beg - ging for one more

mp

do if we were through?
chance, one chance once more.

1 (Tacet)   2 (Tacet)

f

Verse

I know___ life___ has man - y a twist   Lov-ing you___ is the

mp

I Should Care

Words & Music by Sammy Cahn, Axel Stordahl & Paul Weston

Nina Never Knew

Words by Milton Drake
Music by Louis Alter

When I kissed her hand, why dreams be-gan to stir deep down in-side of her!

When I whis-pered things that Ni - na nev - er heard, _____ Ni - na's heart took

wings with ev-'ry ten-der word. _____ Then sud-den-ly she clung to me; she

learned to love some - how. And I'm so glad that Ni - na Nev - er Knew till

1.
now. _____

2.
now. _____

125

Chances Are

Words by Al Stillman
Music by Robert Allen

Moderately, with great warmth

Chanc-es Are 'cause I wear a sil-ly grin, The mo-ment you come in - to view, Chanc-es Are you think that I'm in love with you. Just be-cause my com-po-sure sort of slips, the mo-ment that your lips meet

Polka Dots And Moonbeams

Words by Johnny Burke
Music by Jimmy Van Heusen

Moderately

Mississippi Mud

Words & Music by Harry Barris

It's A Raggy Waltz

Music by Dave Brubeck

It's a raggy waltz, a raggy waltz, a raggy waltz
That I'm gonna dance with you.
Now that you've heard this very funny beat
Let me see if you can feel it in your feet.
Yeah, you've got it! Startin' to swing!
Just forget everything,
Raggy waltzin' with me.
It's not a waltz that's Viennese,
Johann Strauss 'twould never please.

It's a raggy waltz, a raggy waltz, a raggy waltz,
And no other dance will do.
And when the dance is through
You're gonna say,
"Never stop romancin', dancin' in this way
Makes me love you."
Out on the floor you'll be askin' for more
Raggy waltzin' with me.
Come dance with me.

135

waltz, a rag-gy waltz, and no oth-er dance will do.___ And when the

dance is through you're gon-na say, "Nev-er stop ro-manc-in', danc-in' in this

way makes me love you." Out on the floor you'll be ask-in' for more, rag-gy

waltz-in' with me. Come dance with me.

You've Changed

Words by Bill Carey
Music by Carl Fischer

CHORUS: Slowly

YOU'VE CHANGED, that spar - kle in your eyes is

gone, Your smile is just a care - less yawn, You're

break - ing my heart, YOU'VE CHANGED; _____ YOU'VE

CHANGED, Your kiss - es now are so bla - se, You're

139

bored with me in ev - 'ry way, I can't un - der-stand, __ YOU'VE CHANGED; __

__ You've for - got - ten the words, __ "I love __

__ you", _____ each mem - o - ry __ that we've shared. __ You ig -

nore ev - 'ry star _____ a - bove _____ you, _____ I can't

Everything Happens To Me

Words by Tom Adair
Music by Matt Dennis

try to give a part-y and the guy up-stairs com-plains, I guess I'll go thru life just catch-in'

colds and miss-in' trains___ EV - 'RY-THING HAP - PENS TO ME___ I

nev - er miss a thing, I've had the meas - les and the mumps, and

ev - 'ry time I play an ace my part - ner al - ways trumps, I

tel - e - graphed and phoned, I sent an "Air - mail Spec - ial" too, Your

ans - wer was "Good - by," And there was ev - en pos - tage due, I

fell in love just once and then it had to be with you ——

EV - 'RY-THING HAP - PENS TO ME —— I

Lover Man (Oh Where Can You Be)

Words & Music by Jimmy Davies, Roger Ram Ramirez & Jimmy Sherman

SOUL ROCK 4
2 & 3

I don't wish for rich - es,

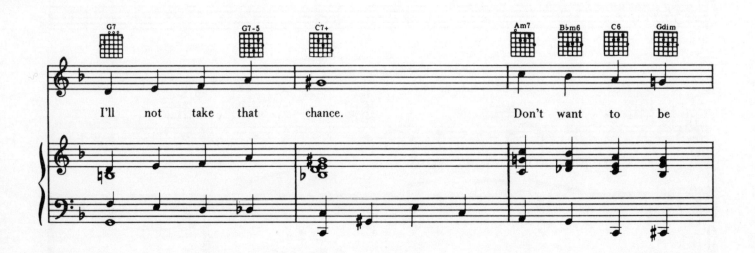

I'll not take that chance.   Don't want to be

fa - mous, I on - ly want ro - mance.

I don't know why but I'm feel-ing so sad.__ I long to try some-thing

I've nev-er had,__ Nev-er had no kiss - in' Oh, what I've been miss- in'.

LOV-ER MAN, oh where can you be? The night is cold, and I'm

so all a-lone,___ I'd give my soul just to call you my own,___

Got a moon a-bove me, but no one to love me, LOV-ER MAN, oh where can you

be? I've heard it said that the thrill of ro-mance can

be like a heav-en-ly dream, I go to bed with a

pray'r that you'll make love to me, Strange as it seems.

Some day we'll meet and you'll dry all my tears,___ Then whis-per sweet lit - tle

things in my ears,___ Hug-gin' and a kiss-in', Oh what we've been miss-in',

LOV-ER MAN, oh where can you be? be?

The Lady Sings The Blues

Words by Billie Holiday
Music by Herbie Nichols

Slow Blues

LA — DY SINGS THE BLUES, _____ she's got them bad, _____ she feels so sad. Wants _____ the world to know _____ just what the blues is all a-bout. _____

she feels so sad, But now ____ the world will know, she's nev - er gon - na sing them no more. ____ no ____ more. ____

The Girl From Ipanema (Garota De Ipanema)

Original Words by Vinicius De Moraes English Lyrics by Norman Gimbel
Music by Antonio Carlos Jobim

Sweet Sue–Just You

Words by Will J. Harris
Music by Victor Young

JAZZ ROCK 1 2+3

158

No-one else it seems ___ ev - er shares my dreams ___ And with-

out you, dear, I don't know what I'd do, ___ In this heart of mine ___

___ you live all the time ___ Sweet Sue, ___ Just

You. ___ Ev - 'ry You. ___

poco rit.

159

Fever

Words & Music by John Davenport & Eddie Cooley

tight.   FE -VER   in the morn-ing,   FE -VER all   through the

1.2.3.4.5.   **Interlude - after 2nd Verse only**

night. Ev - 'ry-bod - y's   got the FE - VER   That is some-thing
(last time)

you all know   FE -VER is - n't   such a new thing FE VER start-ed long__ a - go.

Additional Verses

Verse 3:   Romeo loved Juliet,
Juliet she felt the same.
When he put his arms around her, he said,
"Julie, baby you're my flame."

Chorus: Thou givest fever, when we kisseth
FEVER with thy flaming youth.
FEVER – I'm afire
FEVER, yea I burn forsooth.

Verse 4:   Captain Smith and Pocahantas
Had a very mad affair
When her Daddy tried to kill him, she said,
"Daddy-o don't you dare."

Chorus: Give me fever, with his kisses,
FEVER when he holds me tight.
FEVER – I'm his Missus
Oh Daddy won't you treat him right.

Verse 5:   Now you've listened to my story
Here's the point that I have made.
Chicks were born to give you FEVER
Be it fahreheit or centigrade.

Chorus: They give you FEVER, when you kiss them
FEVER if you live and learn.
FEVER – till you sizzle
What a lovely way to burn.

Take The 'A' Train

Words & Music by Billy Strayhorn

To go to Sug-ar Hill 'way up in Har-lem. _____ If _____ you miss the "A" train, _____ You'll find you've missed the quick-est way to Har-lem. _____ Hur-ry, _____ get on now it's

com-ing_____ Lis - ten____ to those rails a-

thrum-ming_____ All 'board!_____ get on the

"A" train _____ Soon you will be on Sug-ar Hill in

Har - lem._____ Har - lem._____

Georgia On My Mind

Words by Stuart Gorrell
Music by Hoagy Carmichael

One Note Samba (Samba De Uma Nota So)

Original Words by N. Mendonca English Lyrics by Jon Hendrick
Music by Antonio Carlos Jobim

JASS BOSSONOVA

Meditation (Meditacao)

Original Words by Newton Mendonca English Lyrics by Norman Gimbel
Music by Antonio Carlos Jobim

far a-way_____ I have on-ly to close my eyes_____ and you are

back to stay_____ I_____ just think of you_____

And the sad-ness that miss-ing you brings Soon is gone and this heart of mine

sings. Yes_____ I love you so_____ And

that for me is all I need to know_____ I_____

I'm Beginning To See The Light

Words & Music by Harry James, Duke Ellington, Johnny Hodges & Don George

af - ter - glow,_ Or can-dle-light on the mis-tle - toe,_ But

now when you turn the lamp down low_ I'm be - gin-ning to see the light.

_ Used to ram - ble thru the park_

Sha - dow box - ing in the dark_ Then you came and

Stars Fell On Alabama

Words by Mitchell Parish
Music by Frank Perkins

dra - ma, we kissed in a field of white, and stars fell on Al - a -

ba - ma last night. I can't for-get the

glam - our, your eyes held a ten-der light, and stars fell on Al - a -

ba - ma last night. I nev - er planned in my im - a - gi -

177

Violets For Your Furs

Words by Tom Adair
Music by Matt Dennis

Will You Still Be Mine?

Words by Tom Adair
Music by Matt Dennis

A Sunday Kind Of Love

Words & Music by Barbara Belle, Louis Prima, Anita Leonard & Stan Rhodes

love that's on the square. ___ Can't seem to find some - bod - y to care. ___

I'm on a lone - ly road that leads me no - where. ___ I need a Sun - day kind of

love. _____ I do my Sun - day dream - ing and

all my Sun - day schem - ing ev - 'ry min - ute, ev - 'ry hour, ___ ev - 'ry day. I'm

A Taste Of Honey

Words by Ric Marlow
Music by Bobby Scott

So Nice

Music & Original Lyrics by Marcos Valle & Paulo Sergio Valle
English Lyrics by Norman Gimbel

Relaxed Bossa Nova

then give his heart__ to me.   Some-one who's read-y to   give love a start__ with me.

Oh   yes,_____   that would be so   nice._____

____   Should it   be   you and me,   I   could see   it   would be

nice.   nice._____

Imagination

Words by Johnny Burke
Music by Jimmy Van Heusen

Moderately

Let's Get Away From It All

Music by Matt Dennis
Words by Tom Adair

A Night In Tunisia

Music by Frank Paparelli & John 'Dizzy' Gillespie
Words by Raymond Leveen

199

200

202

I'll Remember April

Words & Music by Don Raye, Gene de Paul & Patricia Johnson

I'll Be Around

Words & Music by Alec Wilder

8 BEAT (2) SOUL 3 @ 100

Early Autumn

Words by Johnny Mercer
Music by Ralph Burns & Woody Herman

Snootie Little Cutie

Words & Music by Bob Troup

Slightly Out Of Tune (Desafinado)

English Lyric by Jon Hendricks & Jessie Cavanaugh
Music by Antonio Carlos Jobim

Cute

Words by Stanley Styne
Music by Neal Hefti

Adios

English Words by Eddie Woods
Music & Spanish Words by Enric Madriguera

Don't Worry 'bout Me

Words by Ted Koehler
Music by Rube Bloom

CHORUS

Don't wor-ry 'bout me,_____ I'll get a - long;_____ For-

get a - bout me,_____ be hap-py, my love._____ Let's say that

our lit-tle show is ov-er and so, The sto - ry ends;_____ Why not call it a day the

sen - si-ble way, And still be friends._____ 'Look out for your-self'_____ should

be the rule;____ Give your heart and your love to who - ev - er you love, Don't

be a fool.____ Dar - ling, why should you cling to some fad - ing thing that

used to be?_____ If you can for - get,_____ Don't wor - ry 'bout

me. Don't me.____

I Ain't Got Nobody
(And There's Nobody Cares For Me)

Words & Music by Roger Graham & Spencer Williams

me?_____ I'll sing sweet love songs, hon-ey, all the

time, if you'll come and be my sweet ba - by mine, 'Cause

I_____ ain't got no - bo - dy, And there's no - bo - dy

cares for me._____ me._____

East Of The Sun (And West Of The Moon)

Words & Music by Brooks Bowman

stars we'll find A har-mo-ny of life to a love-ly tune,

East of the sun and west of the moon,

dear, East of the sun and west of the

1 moon.

2 moon.

235

The Night We Called It A Day

Words by Tom Adair
Music by Matt Dennis

lov-ers' meet-ings, ro-man-tic greet-ings, To my mis-for-tune, I found this a' lie, For it was night when you whis-pered "Good-bye," A night of mad-ness that turned to sad-ness, much too soon: _____

237

See See Rider

Words & Music by Gertrude 'Ma' Rainey

A - bout this let - ter   That I will write   I hope he will re - mem - ber

when he re - ceives it. See   CHORUS   See Ri - der ____

See   what ____ you have done   Lawd, Lawd, Lawd,

Made me love you   now your girl done come ____

CHORUS 2:
I'm goin' away baby, won't be back till Fall, Lawd, Lawd, Lawd.
Goin' away baby, won't be back till Fall.
If I find me a good man I won't be back at all.

CHORUS 3:
I'm gonna buy me a pistol just as long as I am tall, Lawd, Lawd, Lawd.
Kill my man and catch the Cannon Ball.
If he don't have me he won't have no girl at all.

Hey Lawdy Mama

Words & Music by Clive Reed

got a mouth full of gold ____

____ Ev - 'ry time he kiss __ me, makes my blood __ go

cold. ____ Now the

door. ____

VERSE 2:
Now the man I love, the man I long to see
Hey Lawdy Mama, little pretty Mama
The man I love, the man I long to see
He's in Cincinatti and he won't write to me.

VERSE 3:
Now the man I love got his feet right on the ground
Hey Lawdy Mama, little pretty Mama
The man I love got his feet right on the ground
He's tailor made, he ain't no hand me down.

VERSE 4:
I'm down and out, ain't got a friend in the world
Hey Lawdy Mama, hey pretty Mama
I'm down and out, ain't got a friend in the world
I know I've been a fool for being someone else's girl.

VERSE 5:
When I had money, I had money to spend
Hey Lawdy Mama, little pretty Mama
When I had money, I had money to spend
Every time I left home, I had a brand new friend.

VERSE 6:
Soon this morning, about a quarter to four
Hey Lawdy Mama, little pretty Mama
Soon this morning, about a quarter to four
You brought your new girl right up to my door.

JAZZ ROCK/SOUL
SLOW SOUL BALL AS SET

If I Had You

Words & Music by Ted Shapiro, Jimmy Campbell & Reg Connelly

I'm Gettin' Sentimental Over You

Words by Ned Washington   Additional Words by Reg Howard
Music by Geo. Bassman

The Lonesome Road

Words by Gene Austin
Music by Nathaniel Shilkret

Look down, look down that lone - some road,___ Be-
(True) love, true love, what have I done,___ That

fore you trav - el on.___ Look up, look
you should treat me so?___ You caus - ed

up and seek yo' mak - er 'Fore Gabri - el blows his
me to walk and talk, like I nev - er did be-

horn. _____ fore. _____ Wea - ry to - tin' such a

load, Tredg - ing down that lone - some road. Look

down, look down that lone - some road _____ Be - fore you

trav - el on. _____ True on. _____

Good Time Flat Blues

Words & Music by Spencer Williams

Runs a good time flat Sel - lin' booze and sing - in' blues Down where she's at The oth - er day I heard her say things are get - ting tough Now the cops done made me stop Oh my they treat me rough.

CHORUS

Can't sell no whis-ky   I can't sell no   gin,
The snow is fall-ing   Ice is on the   ground,
Cops on the cor-ner   got his eyes on   me,
I can't keep o-pen,   gon-na close the   shack,

Can't sell no whis-key   I can't sell no
The snow is fall-in',   Ice is on the
Cop's on the cor-ner,   got his eyes on
I can't keep o-pen,   gon-na close the

gin,   Ain't got no mo-ney
ground,   If I ain't luck-y
me,   And my boot-leg-ger
shack,   The Chief of Po-lice

256

to buy my win - ter coal,
I'm gon - na hit the trail,
He keeps them all a - way,
done tore my play - house down,

Can't make a dol - lar to save my dog - gone soul,
I'll do some steal - in' and then I will land in jail.
I'm so down-heart-ed I've got the blues to - day.
No use in griev - in', I'm gon - na leave this town.

The Mood I'm In

Words & Music by Pete King & Paul Francis Webster

1. I like to feel fan - cy free, I like to live young,
2. I like to hear op - 'ra or I like to read Joyce,

I like the old mer - ry - go - round.
I'm not the pre - dict - a - ble kind.

I like to play lov - er, But don't like to get stung,
What - ev - er the op - tion Is what - ev - er the choice

looks like the right one And waltz down the aisle with cha-grin You see my friends it all de-pends on the mood I'm in. I may

The Music Goes Round And Around

Words by Red Hodgson
Music by Edward Farley & Michael Riley

265

Am E7 Am E7 Am E7 Am G D7
mu-sic goes down a-round be-low, be-low, be-low, Dee-dle-dee ho-ho-ho,
G9 C♯dim Dm7 Em G7 C Dm Cdim C
Lis-ten to the no-tes come out. I push the oth-er valve down. The
C/E Cdim Dm7 C♯dim G7 G9 Em
mu-sic goes 'round and a-round. Whoa-ho-ho-ho-ho-ho, and it comes out
1 C D7 D7(♭5) G7
here. She
2 C G7 C Dm C
here.
ff

My Very Good Friend The Milkman

Words by Johnny Burke
Music by Harold Spina

Cer-tain peo-ple of my ac-quaint-ance Seem ve-ry con-cern'd a-bout you and me. They're try-ing to be nice. They're go-ing out of their way. They of-fer me ad-vice; There must be some-thing in what they say._____ My ve-ry good friend the

Pennies From Heaven

Words by John Burke
Music by Arthur Johnston

Perdido

Music by Juan Tizol
Words by Harry Lenk and Ervin Drake

Summertime Blues

Words & Music by Eddie Cochran & Jerry Capehart

I'm a - gon - na raise a fuss, I'm a - gon - na raise a hol - ler, A-bout a-

work - in' all sum - mer just to try to earn a dol - lar, Ev - 'ry

time I call my Ba - by, Try to get a date, My boss says, "No dice, Son, you got - ta work late,"

Some-times I won-der what I'm a-gon-na do,__ But there ain't no cure for the Sum-mer-time__ Blues.

2.   A well my
3.   (I'm gon-na)

Mom 'n' Pa-pa told me, "Son, you got-ta make some mo-ney,   If you
take__ two__ weeks__ Gon-na have a fine va-ca-tion,   I'm gon-na

want-ta use the car to go a-rid-in' next__ Sun-day,"   Well, I
take__ my__ prob-lem to the U-ni-ted Na-tions!   Well, I

tacet
Spoken

did-n't go to work___ Told the boss I was sick "Now you can't___ use the car 'cause you
called___ my___ Con-gress-man and he___ said (quote) "I'd___ like to help you, Son, but you're

F

did-n't work a lick."___ Some-times I won-der what I'm a-gon-na do,___ But there
too young to vote."___

G7

C   G7 C

1

F   G   C

ain't no cure for the Sum-mer-time Blues.   3. I'm gon-na

2   F   G   C   F   G   C

Sunny

Words & Music by Bobby Hebb

bright days are here____ my sun - ny one____ shines so sin - cere,____} Oh
all ____ and all _____ Now I feel ____ ten feet tall. _____}

Sun - ny one so true,____ I love you.____

3. Sun - ny, ____ thank you for the
4. Sun - ny, ____ thank you for that

truth you've let me see.____ Sun - ny, ____
smile up - on your face.____ Sun - ny, ____

The Touch Of Your Lips

Words & Music by Ray Noble

CHORUS

do. The touch of your lips up - on my brow; Your

lips that are cool and sweet; Such

ten - der - ness lies in their soft ca - ress, My

heart for - gets to beat. The touch of your hands

Lazybones
Words & Music by Johnny Mercer & Hoagy Carmichael

live long day.____ You won't ever change no matter what I say,____ You're just made that way.

in the town, ____ Where they have to hustle till the day is thro'____ They can't shirk like you.

A7 F#o C# A+ D   G   Bb7 E7b5 A7   Bb7 E7b5 A7   D G D

REFRAIN Slowly and Drowsily

La - zy bones, Sleep-in' in the sun, How you 'spec' to get your day's work done?

D   G   D   G   D   G A+ D   D7

Nev-er get your day's work done,   Sleep-in' in the noon-day sun.   La - zy bones,

Eo Ao E7 Am Em   E7b5   A7 G   D   D   G
                                   A7

sleepin' in the shade, How you 'spec' to get your corn meal made? Nev-er get your corn meal made

D   G   D   G A+ D   D7   Eo Ao E7 Am Em

Basin Street Blues

Words & Music by Spencer Williams

band's there to meet us, Old friends to greet us,

Where all the black and the white folks meet,— This is Ba - sin Street:

CHORUS

Ba - sin Street is the street— Where dark e - lite— al - ways meet,— in

New Or - leans,— lan' of dreams, You'll nev - er know how nice it seems or just how much it real - ly means:

That Ole Devil Called Love

Words & Music by Doris Fisher & Allan Roberts

CHORUS

Hit The Road Jack

Words & Music by Percy Mayfield

guess if you say so _____ I'd have to pack my things and go (that's right) Hit the

Cm   G7   Cm

road _ Jack and don't you come back no more, no more, no more, no more, Hit the

Cm   Ab7   G7+   Cm

1

road _ Jack and don't you comeback no more _____ Hit the

Ab7   Cm

2

dim.

don't you come back no more   don't you come back no

dim.

Ab7   Cm   Ab7   Cm

more _____

Bill Bailey Won't You Please Come Home

Traditional

Lonesome (Si Tu Vois Ma Mère)

Composed by Sydney Bechet

303

Is You Is, Or Is You Ain't (Ma' Baby)

Words & Music by Billy Austin & Louis Jordan

How Ya Baby

Words by J C Johnson
Music by Thomas Waller

All Or Nothing At All

Words & Music by Arthur Altman & Jack Lawrence

Moderato

The Beatles

Enya

Phil Collins

Van Morrison

Bob Dylan

Sting

Paul Simon

Tracy Chapman

Eric Clapton

Pink Floyd

New Kids On The Block

Bryan Adams

Tina Turner

Elton John

Bee Gees

Whitney Houston

AC/DC

Bringing you the
words

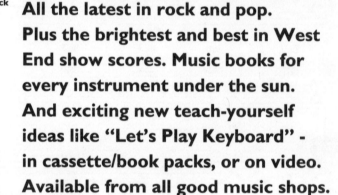

All the latest in rock and pop. Plus the brightest and best in West End show scores. Music books for every instrument under the sun. And exciting new teach-yourself ideas like "Let's Play Keyboard" - in cassette/book packs, or on video. Available from all good music shops.

and
music

Music Sales' complete catalogue lists thousands of titles and is available free from your local music shop, or direct from Music Sales Limited. Please send a cheque or postal order for £1.50 (for postage) to:

Music Sales Limited
Newmarket Road,
Bury St Edmunds,
Suffolk IP33 3YB

Buddy

Five Guys Named Moe

Les Misérables

West Side Story

Phantom Of The Opera

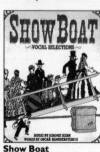
Show Boat

The Rocky Horror Show

**Bringing you the
world's best music.**

1/95 (19347)